# Birds of Prey
## on the Colorado Plateau

By Steven W. Carothers and Dorothy A. House

INTRODUCTION                                                      3

RELATIONSHIPS AMONG THE RAPTORS                                  5

BIRDS OF PREY ON THE PLATEAU                                     6

RAPTORIAL ADAPTATIONS                                           15

CHANGING HABITATS AND ENDANGERED SPECIES                        26

SOME FINAL THOUGHTS                                             42

RAPTORS OF THE COLORADO PLATEAU-LISTING                         44

AUTHORS' NOTE                                                   47

MUSEUM OF NORTHERN ARIZONA

*Above: Swainson's hawk of the* Buteo *genus. Photograph by W. Perry Conway*
*Opposite, top: Soaring California condor. Photograph by David Clendenen*
*Opposite, bottom: Great horned owl. Photograph by Rich Kirchner*

# INTRODUCTION

In the late 1800s, gold prospectors in the remote Colorado Plateau canyon country were a nervous lot—often prowling unknown terrain half-starved, uncertain of their location, and constantly fearful of attack by unfriendly Indians. The philosophy of "shoot first, ask questions later" had its origins in the paranoia intrinsic to life on the frontier. There should be no surprise, then, when we read naturalist Herbert H. Brown's account of an unfortunate encounter between three prospectors and the last known California condors near Grand Canyon.

While cooking breakfast over a campfire on a cool March morning in 1881, Bill Johnson, Joe Henderson, and Miles Noyes were startled by looming images on the cliffs above. Assuming that they were about to be attacked by Indians, the men scrambled for their Winchesters. But before they could get off a shot, and to their considerable astonishment, the "Indians" spread huge wings, launched themselves from the cliff, and soared directly over camp. Asking no questions, one of the men took aim and fired a quick rifleshot. His target, an immense bird, reeled and tumbled to its death on the rocks below.

By Brown's account, "The men had no rule, so measured [the bird] with a gun. It was over a gun length in height and more than three gun lengths in the spread of its wings." Later, the men described the bird as being dark brown with purplish warts on its neck. This, combined with its extraordinary size, convinced Brown that the bird was a California condor—the first and one of the few ever recorded on or near the Colorado Plateau. With a wingspan that can exceed nine feet, the California condor is the largest North American member of a group of birds called "raptors." Also referred to as "birds of prey," the raptors include winged predators like eagles, hawks, falcons, and owls, as well as the less glamorous, carrion-eating vultures and condors.

Few birds have so fascinated humans as these meat-eating hunters. Part of the fascination results from the striking physiological and anatomical equipment that most birds of prey have acquired to become swift, efficient killers. Although not closely related, the main groups of raptors share similar physical characteristics that have evolved independently as a result of similar life habits. They all, for example, possess fierce hooked beaks to tear flesh. And in raptors, nature has fine-tuned body streamlining, sight and hearing, and general sensory perception to a degree unparalleled among other bird groups. These specialized, often superb, adaptations enable birds of prey to locate, seize, and consume a broad array of animals—from insects and fish to small mammals and other birds.

In recent decades, we have come to recognize that the raptors, from their position at the top of the food web, provide us with a commanding view of the overall health of the ecosystem they occupy. If the birds of prey and the scavenger vulture populations are high and healthy, it can be assumed that their primary food sources are healthy. If some of the raptors are declining in numbers, an ecological search for the cause often uncovers levels of decay in the area's general environmental health. Much attention has been focused over the last few years on the peril faced by this nation's birds of prey—most notably spotted owls, bald eagles, peregrine falcons, condors, and goshawks. These species play a critical role because they serve as barometers of ecological health and change on the Colorado Plateau.

Ranking as one of the West's great geological provinces, the Colorado Plateau is an elevated, generally arid region that covers some 130,000 square miles between the Rocky Mountains and the Great Basin. Topographically and ecologically varied, the plateau encompasses high-desert mesas, forested mountains, deep canyons, and limited, but productive, riparian woodlands. It includes parts of four states (Colorado, New Mexico, Arizona, and Utah) and boasts the largest concentration of national parks and monuments in the country—including Grand Canyon, Zion, Bryce Canyon, and two dozen more. Millions of acres are blanketed by fifteen national forests, among them the

Coconino, the Kaibab, the Dixie, the Manti-La Sal, the Uncompaghre, and the Cibola. Each forest embraces a range of woodland types, from piñon and juniper at the lower elevations, up through ponderosa pine, to mixed conifers in the higher reaches. The Colorado River and its myriad tributaries drain the region, but most waterways are ephemeral in nature, dry much of the year. Few natural lakes can be found, but several reservoirs, including 186-mile-long Lake Powell, snake across a landscape dominated by high-desert grassland and shrubs.

The diversity of habitats found on the plateau supports twenty two species of breeding raptors and another ten species that are either occasional transients or regular winter visitors. Yet another species, the California condor, has vanished from the area during historical times. How these birds have evolved to succeed as hunters and scavengers and how some of them have responded to both natural and man-caused changes on the plateau are the subjects of our story.

*Map by Mike Donaldson*

# RELATIONSHIPS AMONG THE RAPTORS

Very little is revealed about the evolution of raptorial birds in the fossil record. However, sufficient evidence exists to suggest that owls, at least, have been around a very long time, perhaps 70 to 80 million years. The oldest known undisputed fossil owl, *Ogygoptynx wetmorei*, dates from some 60 million years ago. It was discovered on the Colorado Plateau and may represent a distant common ancestor linking the two living families of owls. North American hawks and eagles appear to be less ancient, with hawks dating back about 25 to 30 million years and eagles about 10 million years.

*The golden eagle is the most formidable bird of prey on the plateau. Photograph by Dick Canby*

The taxonomic relationships among these birds are vigorously debated and remain something of a scientific mystery. The fact that owls, hawks, eagles, falcons, condors, and vultures are collectively termed "raptors" stems from a 1872 publication by Elliott Coues, *Key to the North American Birds*. Because Coues's classification system was based on what he perceived to be shared physical characteristics, he concluded that all birds of prey descended from a common, distant ancestor. He classed these birds in the order Raptores, which he divided into three suborders: the owls, the

New World vultures, and all the remaining birds of prey. Although subsequent taxonomic studies have shown Coues's assumption to be incorrect, his convention still stands informally, and we continue to refer to all such birds as "raptors."

Current interpretation of genetic relationships within the raptors indicates that none of Coues's original three groups are closely related, but instead represent three separate lines of evolution. The owls, for example, appear to have more affinity to the Caprimulgidae family of goatsuckers, nighthawks, and whip-poor-wills than to the other raptors. Vultures and condors appear to be more akin to the storklike birds. While these relationships are being worked out, most ornithologists adhere to a formal classification system that recognizes two large and distinct raptorial orders: the Falconiformes and the Strigiformes. The Falconiformes include the families Accipitridae (osprey, hawks, and eagles), Falconidae (falcons), and Cathartidae (vultures and condors). The order Strigiformes, or owls, is split into two families: Tytonidae (barn-owls) and Strigidae (all remaining owls).

*Rough-legged hawk, one of the soaring buteo hawks. Photograph by W. Perry Conway*

# BIRDS OF PREY ON THE PLATEAU

*Bald eagle, normally a winter visitor to the Colorado Plateau. Photograph by Denver A. Bryan*

"What kind of hawk was that?" How many times have you uttered that question under your breath or heard it asked out loud? It is a rare day on the Colorado Plateau, whether you are driving from one national park or monument to the next, taking in the view from a scenic point, hiking a trail, or sitting in a forest glade, that "hawks" of one kind or another are not present to share the scene.

We offer here a list of the most common raptors on the Colorado Plateau. To identify one of these birds in the field, you should pay attention to the habitat within which the bird is seen and to a few characteristics of flight, behavior, and body style.

The difficult-to-see nocturnal owls are most readily distinguished by their characteristic hoots, barks, and screams.

The raptors described below could be encountered in any of the plateau's four states, north or south, east or west. Most of these species prefer certain kinds of habitats—whether it be open grasslands, forests, cliffsides, or large bodies of water. Associating a specific bird with a specific habitat increases the odds of identifying it, but there are no guarantees. Birds do not feel compelled to be where you most expect to find them, and a few species, like the red-tailed hawk and the turkey vulture, appear to be happy just about anywhere.

*Osprey.* A large-sized hawk with wings that seem to bend sharply in the middle, the osprey exhibits stark black and white coloration. It is one of two raptors (the bald eagle is the other) that will actually dive into and under the water in pursuit of a fish. This bird almost always nests high in a large tree near open water, particularly lakes, where its primary diet of fish is easily found.

*The osprey, a fish-eating hawk. Photograph by W. Perry Conway*

*Bald Eagle.* This species and its cousin, the golden eagle, are the largest birds of prey found on the Colorado Plateau. The adult bald eagle with its dark body and striking white head and tail is hard to miss or confuse with anything else. Immature bald and golden eagles, however, do resemble one another, both being dark with white markings on their heads and tails. If the bird is seen around water, though, chances are it is a bald eagle. Bald eagles rarely visit the plateau during summer, but in winter they pass through on their way to and from breeding grounds and concentrate around lakes. During January and February, twenty to thirty bald eagles at a time can be found near Lake Mary and Mormon Lake just outside of Flagstaff.

Much to the distress of ospreys, adult bald eagles often wait for the ospreys to catch a fish, then, in what can be a great aerial battle, harass the ospreys into dropping their prey. They will even roll in under the ospreys and tear fish from their talons. Bald eagles also feed on carrion if given the chance. Just this spring, wildlife authorities in southern Utah investigated a poisoned deer carcass that was found with the remains of several bald eagles scattered around it. The poisoner probably was after coyotes; he killed endangered eagles instead.

*Northern harrier's flight over carrion.*
*Photograph by John Hendrickson*

*Northern Harrier (Marsh Hawk).* A little smaller than an osprey, the adult male harrier is gray overall, with sharp, black wing tips and a white band at the base and on top of its tail. Females and juveniles are a dull brown with a similar tail band. Found primarily over marshes, open fields, and meadows, the harriers are characterized by their "hovering" flight pattern, being one of only a few raptors that appear to do this. This near-stationary flight and the erratic, acrobatic, and swooping dives of the male harrier set this bird apart.

*Harriers favor marsh habitats. Photograph by W. Perry Conway*

## HAWKS OF THE DEEP FOREST

The northern goshawk, the Cooper's hawk, and the sharp-shinned hawk of the genus Accipiter (short-winged hawks) are beautifully adapted for a predatory lifestyle in the deep forest. They rarely soar when hunting; indeed, their bodies are poorly designed for the soaring flight typical of most other hawks and eagles. Their short, rounded wings; compact, deeply muscled breasts; and long tails permit sudden acceleration and instantaneous maneuverability. The accipiter hawks are the aerial hunters frequently seen diving headlong into dense thickets in pursuit of prey. When hatched, all young accipiters have yellow eyes that turn orange and finally red as the birds mature. These hawks avoid open areas, preferring the heavily wooded forest, and are most frequently seen as a blur crossing a forest road or trail. When sitting, they appear more nervous and flighty than the calmer broad-winged hawks. The difference in size between the sexes is extreme in these birds, with the females being up to a third larger than the males.

*Northern Goshawk.* About the same size as a raven, the northern goshawk is the largest of the three accipiter species found on the plateau. The adults have solid steel-gray backs and gray underparts streaked with black. Juveniles are a streaked brown above and below. Although a large part of this bird's diet consists of other forest birds, the goshawk stands unchallenged as the principal predator of the Kaibab, Abert, and red squirrels of the ponderosa pine and mixed conifer forests of the Colorado Plateau.

*Cooper's Hawk.* The "coop" is almost as big as the goshawk; in fact, the largest female Cooper's hawks are slightly bigger than male goshawks. Like the goshawk, the Cooper's hawk has a steel-gray back, but its breast is streaked light brown. Although these birds will nest in conifer forests and sometimes feed on the smaller red squirrels, chipmunks, and ground squirrels found there, Cooper's hawks are the most common nesting raptors of the plateau's wooded streamside areas. In that habitat, they seem to prefer a diet of other birds.

We have found more nests of the Cooper's hawk twenty feet or more up a large cottonwood or sycamore tree than in any other tree type. The grayish brown flash of a hawk seen in dense riparian woodlands is most likely this bird.

*Top: A goshawk darts through the forest.*
*Photograph by Rick Kline for*
*Cornell Laboratory of Ornithology*
*Bottom: Cooper's hawk.*
*Photograph by J. Hoffman for VIREO*

*Sharp-shinned Hawk.* Smallest of the forest hawks, "sharpies" are about the size of a mourning dove but more streamlined. They look almost exactly like the Cooper's hawk, with the notable exception that their tail tips are more square or blockish, while those of the "coop" are rounded. Although the sharpies are known to breed in the high mountains of the Colorado Plateau, they are less commonly seen in the summertime than either of the two larger accipiters. Sharpies seem to reach their highest densities in winter, especially in urban areas where they seek out homes where bird feeders are kept full. A couple of sharp-shinned hawks can quickly decimate a well-attended feeding station. Their favorite food consists of sparrow-sized birds.

*Red-tailed hawk of the genus* Buteo. *Photograph by Christopher Crowley for Cornell Laboratory of Ornithology*

*A soaring red-tailed hawk. Photograph by John Hendrickson*

## SOARING HAWKS, EAGLES, AND VULTURES OF MEADOWS AND RANGELAND

Typically seen gently soaring a few to several hundred feet above the ground, the golden eagle, the turkey vulture, and the big hawks of the genus Buteo are the most commonly seen birds of prey in open spaces of the plateau. Buteos are members of the "broad-winged" hawk group, and their large, thick wings, broad tails, and seemingly effortless flight easily distinguish them from the "short-winged" hawks of the deep forest. The buteos usually are the birds of prey seen perched on telephone poles and fences along highways. Although buteos often appear to be much larger when flying, their wingspans rarely exceed three feet.

*Red-tailed Hawk.* Red-tails are the most common of all our large hawks, and at least ninety percent of the time, the large soaring hawk you see above you is this species. All of the buteos commonly found on the Colorado Plateau are about the same size and shape, but only adult red-tails have the characteristic reddish brown color on the upper tail. Although this color occurs only on the upper surface, it can be seen from below if the light is right. Body color varies in this species, from the very dark, almost black forms called "melanistic" to near albinos, but red-tails typically are whitish underneath and dark above, with light streaking from the breast down the abdomen. When the wings are extended during flight, a conspicuous dark band of feathers can be seen at the leading edge of each wing. The reddish brown tail, however, is what we look for. Red-tails forage mostly on small and medium-sized mammals and, to a lesser extent, birds. Find an area of relatively open woodlands or desert scrub with abundant cottontail rabbits and you have found red-tailed hawk habitat.

9

*Ferruginous, Swainson's, and Rough-legged Hawks.* If the soaring buteo you see is not a red-tailed hawk, it almost certainly will be one of these three. The buteos are not restricted to any particular habitat; however, open grasslands and sparse woodlands seem to be their favorite environments. Of the three hawks, the ferruginous is the one that will appear to be almost all white, both above and below, with the exception of a rufous (reddish) cinnamon color on the upper wings. Sometimes, a dark, V-shaped band of darker feathers forms on the legs and belly.

Swainson's hawks are quickly distinguished from the others by the distinct rufous breastband beginning just below the neck. This description holds unless a heavily pigmented melanistic form is seen; then, the entire underside looks dark brown. The rough-legged hawk is the only one with a broad, white band on the tail below the rump and a dark band near the tail tip. When seen in flight, the upper outer margins of the wings display distinct white patches.

*Golden Eagle.* The most formidable predator of the open rangelands and sparse woodlands, the golden eagle weighs up to thirteen pounds and boasts a seven-foot wing span, powerful feet the size of a man's fist, and daggerlike talons. It has been known to take down wolves and mule deer. Falconer David Ellis' five-year-old son barely made the safety of the house one day when the family's "pet" eagle decided the youngster looked good enough to eat and charged him. Bizarre incidents like this can happen when such powerful and aggressive animals are raised in captivity and become imprinted on humans.

Goldens are big, strong birds, not easily confused with anything but other eagles. From a distance, if the bird's size does not make identification obvious, look to the wing tips. The primary feathers on eagles are slotted and splayed open far more than those of most other birds of prey.

*Turkey Vulture.* These ubiquitous scavengers are slightly larger than the buteo hawks and are frequently mistaken for them, or for eagles, but identifying vultures is relatively easy. Turkey vultures soar with their wings angled upward in a dihedral, or V-shaped, pattern while most hawks soar with flattened wings. Turkey vultures are black, with unmistakable broad, white margins under their wings and bald, red heads (black in juveniles). The baldness helps to protect carrion eaters from disease-causing bacterial growth that would flourish in matted feathers. If one is unfortunate enough to be very close to them, the first thing noticed is the pungent odor of decaying flesh.

THE FALCONS

The fast-flying falcons, with their relatively long, pointed wings and extended, tapering tails, are distinguished by rapid wing-beats interspersed with short glides. A distinctly notched bill is evident at very close range. Of the four species known from the area, only three—the American kestrel, the peregrine falcon, and prairie falcon—can be seen frequently, but you must know where to look and what to look for. A fourth falcon, the foot-long merlin, is a rare winter resident on the Colorado Plateau, and even experienced ornithologists have difficulty finding and identifying them.

*American Kestrel (Sparrow Hawk).* If the red-tail is the hawk most likely to be noticed by travelers driving through plateau country, the kestrel is the most common falcon. It is often seen perched on roadside fences and transmission wires, occasionally diving to the ground in pursuit of insects or lizards. About the size and shape of a mourning dove, the kestrel is the only hawklike bird with a rufous back or tail and a black and white face. Like the much larger marsh hawk, it will hover in flight.

*Peregrine and Prairie Falcons.* These two species can be very difficult to tell apart, especially if they are seen only briefly during flight. Although the female peregrine is clearly the largest of these birds, the male peregrine and female prairie frequently overlap in size.

The most obvious characteristic distinguishing one species from the other is head coloration. The peregrine has a black head, with wide, dark "sideburns" running down from just below the eyes to the middle of the neck. The prairie falcon has a sandy brown head; a thin, brown mustache; and white eyebrow stripes. For the most part, peregrines are uniformly white under the wings while prairies show blackish patches in the wingpits.

They differ in habitat and food preference, too. The prairie falcon likes open sagebrush and desert grassland terrain where it can find its favored prey—

small mammals and birds. Cliff habitat suitable for nesting must be within a few miles. The peregrine, on the other hand, lives among massive cliffs and hunts avian prey almost exclusively. The more commanding the cliff, the more a peregrine will like the site. Off the Colorado Plateau, the extremes of this are found in cities like Phoenix, Salt Lake, and Denver, where peregrine falcons nest on the window ledges of skyscrapers.

*Right: The prairie falcon's sharp, narrow wings produce speed and maneuverability. Photograph by B.K. Wheeler for VIREO*
*Bottom: Turkey vultures often spread their wings to dry. The white undersides are obvious in flight. Photograph by Robert Campbell*

## THE OWLS

We have identified ten species of owls on the Colorado Plateau, and of these, only three allow themselves to be seen regularly during the day. The other seven, however, can be distinguished by their voices and habitats. If a nocturnal owl is seen in sufficient light to discern physical characteristics, the two most important things to note, besides overall size, are the color of its eyes (brown or yellow) and whether or not the bird has feathers, or "ear tufts," that project from the head and resemble paired horns or ears. The owls on the plateau fall into three primary size classes, measured as standing upright: large (14 to 25 inches), medium (9 to 13 inches), and small (6 to 9 inches). Only three species have brown eyes: the barn-owl, the spotted owl, and the diminutive flammulated owl. All the rest have yellow eyes. The owls notable for their ear tufts are the great horned, the long-eared, and the western screech-owls. Flammulated and short-eared owls have inconspicuous ear tufts. Every owl listed, with the exception of the barn-owl, belongs to the family Strigidae. The barn-owl represents the family Tytonidae.

**Burrowing Owl.** This is the medium-sized owl seen often in twos and threes, standing erect next to a prairie dog or squirrel burrow in broad daylight. It uses the burrow as a refuge if threatened. Burrowing owls reach their highest densities where they can find active or abandoned homes of colonial rodents. Frequently, they will perch on fence posts or rocks, but they rarely stray far from an underground source of protection. The sexes look alike, tawny brown in color with streaked, barred, and spotted markings back and front. Their most distinguishing characteristics are very long legs and a distinct white stripe under the chin.

**Northern Pygmy-owl.** A small owl of the deep forest, the pygmy-owl is the only true diurnal, or daytime, owl besides the burrowing. Black patches and white underfeathers on either side of the neck give this bird the appearance of having an extra set of eyes on the back of its head, a feature thought to have protective benefits if the owl is approached by a predator from behind. The pygmy-owl can also be identified by its rapid, single, mellow whistle note: too-too-too-too-too.

**Great horned Owl.** Although not considered a true diurnal owl, the great horned owl will begin to

*A spotted owl poised to strike. Feathers flare at the last moment to stall flight. Photograph by John Hendrickson*

*Great horned owl. White
raptorial resting or roostin*

12

hunt before dark and continue for a while after dawn, so it can be seen in daylight. Biologists refer to this dusk-to-dawn activity pattern as crepuscular. Largest of all our owls and a voracious predator on any creature of the twilight or nighttime smaller than itself, the great horned owl has prominent ear tufts nearly two inches long. Its voice is the classical hoo! hoo! hoo! we have learned to associate with ghostly sounds of the night. This species is one of the most common of owls found on the Colorado Plateau and may be expanding in distribution and numbers. As deep forests open up from timber cutting, the great horned owl moves into the cleared "edges" and thrives.

*Flammulated Owl.* This is our only small owl with dark eyes. It is the most common owl of the pine and mixed conifer forests on the plateau, and if the hoot you hear is not a great horned owl, it is probably the flammulated. Its voice, a low-pitched, mellow hoot-hoot-hoot, repeated every two to three seconds, is so relatively loud and deep that the first-time observer is usually surprised to find that the source is a tiny, six-inch-high bundle of brown feathers.

*Spotted Owl.* A large owl, but still several inches smaller than a great horned, this is the only large dark-eyed owl of the forest. Almost exclusively found in the thickest of old-growth forests, this relatively tame owl is easily called in by simulating its loud, four-note hoot: whoo-hoo-hoo-whoooo. Males have sufficiently lower pitched hoots to enable a listener to distinguish between the sexes. This species has a heavily spotted breast; a barred belly; and a smooth, rounded head.

*Northern Saw-whet Owl.* This tiny, bright-yellow-eyed moth-eater is unpredictable in its haunts. In some years, you might hear as many as a dozen calling in the San Francisco Peaks area outside of Flagstaff. Some years, they don't show up at all. The saw-whet can be a dark little owl, especially the juveniles, who look so different from the tawny and streaked adults that they were once considered to be a separate species. Its call is a mellow whistle, with a too-too-too-too repeated rapidly, often over 100 times per minute.

*Long-eared Owl.* But for its medium size and reddish brown facial disk, this yellow-eyed owl with long ear tufts looks very much like the larger great horned owl. Its voice reminds one of the hoo-hoo-hoo sound made by blowing over the top of an open beer bottle. When alarmed, long-eared owls also can produce a long, creaking noise that is guaranteed to startle the most experienced of outdoors enthusiasts. This is a fairly rare owl on the Colorado Plateau.

*Western Screech-owl.* This small owl is not very common on the plateau but can be found in some deciduous woodland riparian areas, where it uses flicker holes and natural cavities in cottonwood trees for nests. The species seems to reach its highest densities off the plateau in the riparian woodlands and mesquite bosques of southern Arizona. The voice is described as a "tremolo," the sound of a ball bouncing more and more rapidly over a hard surface. It will also use a single, drawn-out note as a prelude to the primary call, the end of the note being somewhat higher pitched than the beginning.

*Short-eared Owl.* Medium-sized and very rare in our area, this handsome owl has a strongly defined, nearly circular, white facial disk. Black feathers ring its brilliant yellow eyes. Ear tufts are present, but they are small and difficult to see. Its voice is an abrupt wheezing bark or yap: kee-waow, yow, yow. Short-eared owls favor open grassland habitats, where they roost in groups on the ground.

*Barn-Owl.* Looking markedly different from the Strigidae owls, the tawny-colored barn-owl possesses a heart-shaped facial disk, very long legs, and noticeably smooth feathers. Open areas with old buildings are sure to attract this large monkey-faced, brown-eyed owl. Observers fortunate enough to watch the barn-owl's exclusively nighttime movements commonly refer to the "moth-like" quality of its flight. There is nothing gentle about the barn-owl's voice, however. Over fifteen distinct calls have been identified in the species, but it is the shrill, rasping scream, humanlike in pitch, that can set a timid ornithologist's heart pounding and leave nerves unsettled for the remainder of the field trip.

Long-eared owls have prominent ear tufts and nearly circular facial disks. Photograph from MNA Archives

The short-eared owl, identified by his black mask, commonly roosts in the cover of grass. Photograph by W. Perry Conway

# RAPTORIAL ADAPTATIONS

The raptors that hunt by day—hawks, eagles, and falcons—often are referred to collectively as diurnal birds of prey. Owls, because most of them hunt by night, are commonly called nocturnal birds of prey. The two groups have developed specific traits that allow them to excel as either daylight or nighttime predators, but they all share certain adaptations needed for hunting. These include well-developed eyesight for spotting and intercepting prey; strong feet with long, sharp talons for grasping and killing prey; the ability to regularly regurgitate undigested animal parts; and, of course, their characteristically hooked beaks. All raptors, including scavengers, have developed unique flight adaptations that reflect different foraging strategies in different habitats.

## VISION

The keenest instrument of sight known is the eye of the hawk. Birds of prey are so respected for their sharp vision that we use the term "eagle-eyed" as a synonym for extreme perceptual acuity. Although we cannot look through a raptor's eye or know for certain what it sees, researchers studying eye physiology can estimate the relative visual abilities of some of these birds. They believe, for example, that a kestrel's vision is possibly 2.6 times more acute than that of humans and that large buteo hawks, like the red-tailed, may see eight times better. Field observations support these estimates and document extraordinary visual feats. Researchers know that a bald eagle can spot another flying eagle nearly twelve miles away. They also know that a falcon can detect the flash of a white handkerchief from 5,100 feet, nearly a mile away. A few years ago, while rafting with a group of peregrine biologists near Kwagunt Rapid in Grand Canyon, someone with a scope in our party spotted a peregrine falcon flying along the canyon rim. It was silhouetted against the sky some 3,200 feet overhead. As we watched, the bird gathered its wings and plunged into a dive toward the river, an arrow streak intent on one of several diminutive, violet-green swallows and white-throated swifts swirling near our boat. No human could have seen a tiny swallow from 3,200 feet against the backdrop of a canyon floor—but the peregrine did.

This visual acuity, or resolving power, results primarily from two physiological adaptations: the large size of the raptor's eye and the density of visual cells in its retina. Both diurnal and nocturnal birds of prey possess remarkably large eyes for their size. In fact, the eyes fill much of the bird's skull, generally outweighing the brain and often projecting somewhat beyond the contours of the skull. This is particularly true of diurnal birds of prey and may explain why these birds have developed the characteristic hawklike "eyebrow," that bony ridge above the eye that gives hawks and eagles their piercing, angry look. The ridge probably shields the eye, deflecting wind and grit during flight and shading it from the sun's glare. The eyes are so big they can barely be moved in their sockets. To compensate for this ocular immobility, raptors have developed extra vertebrae so they can move and twist their heads with extraordinary flexibility.

Large eyes produce large retinal images, and this certainly contributes to acuity, but even the biggest raptorial eyes are no bigger in size than human eyes. Why, then, do raptors see so much better than we do? The answer lies in the number of visual cells, called cones and rods, that are packed into the retina at the back of the eye. Cones function in bright daylight to distinguish color and produce sharp images. Rods are sensitive to dim light for night vision. Diurnal raptors, the birds that hunt by day, specialize in cones, concentrating a great many of them in their retinas—particularly in a small circular area called the fovea. This is the point on the retina of a vertebrate eye that contains the highest density of visual cells and produces the sharpest image. The human eye has a single fovea with a density of about 200,000 cones per square millimeter. Raptors have two foveae, with cone densities approaching 1,000,000 per square millimeter in some hawks. No other animal is known to have developed a higher concentration. This means that an image cast on a hawk's retina will excite many more visual cells than a comparably sized image on any other animal's retina. But this is only one way in which raptorial vision excels. Compared to other birds, raptors also possess an unusual degree of binocular vision.

Binocular vision, which allows an animal to locate a moving object precisely in three-dimensional space, is produced when the vision fields of both eyes overlap. The more forward facing the eyes, the greater the overlap and the wider the binocular field of vision. Human eyes face directly forward; consequently, a large proportion (144 degrees) of our 180-degree vision field is binocular. The rest is monocular. The pigeon, a typical nonhunting bird with eyes oriented to the sides of its head, commands an impressive total vision field of 340 degrees—but only 24 degrees of it is binocular. Being a prey species, pigeons must be able to watch for attack from every quarter, but they do not need to do this with pinpoint precision. Any nearby movement will cause pigeons to take to the air.

Raptors, on the other hand, have sacrificed the defensive advantage of wide monocular vision for the predatorial advantage of narrower, but more precise, binocular vision. Their more forward-facing eyes enable them to locate moving targets from a considerable distance, lock onto them, and strike with accuracy. Among birds, owls have the greatest percentage of binocular vision—60 to 70 degrees. The kestrel, a falcon, commands about 50 degrees binocular vision, and hawks range from 35 to 50 degrees.

## TALONS

The chief weapons of all hunting birds of prey are their formidable talons. Designed to catch, kill, and carry prey, raptorial feet are the most powerful (and their talons the longest and sharpest) in the bird world. Golden eagles can clutch their victims with a force of two hundred pounds per square inch. A Museum of Northern Arizona biologist experienced this firsthand once, when he found himself writhing on the ground with a full-grown, injured golden eagle clamped to his upper arm. It took four men to pull the bird free—one to pin it to the ground, the other three to pry the talons loose. Raptors lock onto their prey with such force that at times it may be impossible for them to release. Fishermen tell sad stories of finding partial skeletons of drowned ospreys still clutching fish that were too large for them to lift from the water.

*Osprey talons are adapted to firmly grip fish.*
*Photograph by Robert Campbell*

*The bony ridge over this ferruginous hawk's eye provides shade and protection.*
*Photograph by Denver A. Bryan*

*Owls, like this long-eared, have forward-facing eyes. Photograph by D. & M. Zimmerman for VIREO*

*Owl talon. Photograph by Lang Elliott for Cornell Laboratory of Ornithology*

*Young golden eagles already display lethal feet and claws. Photograph by W. Perry Conway*

Unable to let go, unable to takeoff, the ospreys perished.

Like the majority of birds, most raptors have three toes that permanently point forward, and one, called the hallux, that turns backward. The osprey and the owls are exceptions. Since the osprey needs to maintain a secure, evenly distributed grip on slippery, wriggling fish, it can reverse one of its forward toes, swinging it around to the back. This grip is reinforced by rough, spiky projections called spicules on the undersides of its feet, an adaptation shared by other fish-eating raptors, including the bald eagle. Owls, which must catch small mammals in very dim light, also have a reversible toe. They always seize and carry their prey with two toes in front and two in back, probably to increase their odds of success.

Other foot adaptations among raptors include the eagle's particularly long and strong hind talon, which it employs dagger-fashion to pierce the vital organs of captured prey. Eagles and hawks commonly knead captives with their strong toes and talons to kill them.

Large falcons, like the peregrine, use their talons to attack birds in mid-air. If they overtake their quarry after a low-angle pursuit, and the prey bird is small enough, the falcon may snatch it from the air and carry it to the ground or to a perch. However, if the falcon attacks from a high-angle, high-speed dive, called a stoop, it will not attempt to grasp the prey. Instead, it strikes a powerful, often killing, blow with its feet as it passes. If the attack is successful, the falcon either follows the stricken bird to the ground or loops back to catch it in the air. Some observers believe that the glancing blow is delivered with talons balled into a fist, surmising that falcons engage their prey with such speed that if they were to strike with spread talons, they would likely injure, even break, their toes. This theory is challenged, however, by one researcher, Dr. George E. Goslow, Jr., who actually captured peregrine falcon strikes on film. In each case, the falcon raked its target with fully extended talons. Whatever their method, falcons hit with tremendous force. During a museum research expedition several years ago, we watched a cinnamon teal duck literally blast apart in a feathery explosion over the Colorado River when struck by a peregrine in full stoop. The disappointed peregrine searched for several minutes, looking for at least a morsel of food, but the pieces of duck had been swept away by the current.

Vultures and condors do not have characteristic raptor feet. Because they feed exclusively on carrion, these scavengers have much weaker feet than other raptors, and their talons are shorter and blunter. Such feet need do little more than hold down a carcass while it is being pulled apart and devoured.

## PELLETS

Raptors rank among the birds that must regularly regurgitate undigestible material. The ability to do this is essential for birds of prey because they do not discriminate when they bolt down whole animals or parts of animals. Bone, fur, feathers, beaks, claws, teeth—it doesn't matter—everything goes down. The meal is pulverized in the bird's gizzard, and the substances that can be broken down by acids and enzymes move on through the digestive tract. The rest is balled up and expelled by mouth in the form of pellets, or "castings" as they are sometimes called. This happens several hours after the bird eats and must be done before it eats again. Apparently, casting pellets serves the secondary purpose of scouring the bird's throat of residual organic matter that can breed bacteria. Raptors in captivity often sicken, and may even die, if they are fed solely on a diet of digestible meat.

Owls eject more material than do eagles, hawks, or falcons, partly because they are more likely to swallow animals whole and partly because their gastric system is less acidic. Large clusters of pellets often can be found under an owl's favorite roost, giving inquisitive biologists a convenient and harmless way to study the bird's diet.

*Owl pellets contain undigestible material like hair, teeth, and bone. Photograph by Lang Elliott for Cornell Laboratory of Ornithology*

*Owls have a narrow vision field but a larger percentage of binocular vision than other birds. Drawing by Jodi Griffith, from Paul Singer in* The Audubon Society Encyclopedia of North American Birds. *Courtesy of Paul Singer Designs.*

## FLIGHT

All of these adaptions are intriguing; all of them speak to a predatorial way of life based on pursuit and violence, but nothing so catches our imagination as the winged flight of these lethal animals. Most birds fly, but no other bird approaches the majesty of a soaring golden eagle; no other bird surpasses the drama of a hurtling peregrine falcon. In raptors, flight wing structure and body streamlining vary considerably. Each of these adaptations relates directly to the bird's hunting strategy, its prey, and its habitat. The major distinction lies between the slow-flying soaring birds and the high-speed diving birds, but other, more subtle differences exist as well. The adaptations for silent flight in nocturnal birds are in a class by themselves.

Golden eagles, bald eagles, condors, and turkey vultures spend many hours aloft, scouting the landscape for their next meal. The largest hawks, the buteos, also hunt in this manner. To minimize the energy required to fly for long periods at a time, they have developed a wing structure that allows them to soar on rising air currents with very little flapping.

*Soaring birds like the bald eagle have broad, large wings that allow them to stay aloft for long periods with little flapping. Slotted primary feathers slow their flight.*
*Photograph by Denver A. Bryan*

stronger for their weight than any manmade substance. To further reduce weight, birds have eliminated the bulky bladder, needed by mammals to store diluted nitrogenous wastes (urea), by voiding instead concentrated nitrogen bound in inert crystals (uric acid). Birds also save weight by allowing their reproductive organs to atrophy when they are not needed. Some species have shown a 1500-fold increase in the weight of male reproductive organs during the breeding season.

Power promotion, a second series of adaptations, refers to the fact that birds require large amounts of energy to sustain flight. All flying birds possess powerful breast muscles to drive the wings and a strong, well-developed sternum, or breastbone, on which to attach those muscles. To provide sufficient energy for flight, birds have developed, among other things, a high metabolic rate, an energy-rich diet, and heat-conserving plumage.

The soaring raptors have fined-tuned these adaptations for their particular needs. For example, because they do not often beat their wings, their breast muscles are somewhat reduced. On the other hand, wing tendons and ligaments are unusually well developed to allow the birds to hold their wings outstretched for long periods of time with little effort. To strengthen the ends of their wings, the soarers' finger-bones are reinforced with internal struts. The wings are broad and large in relation to the birds' body weight, a condition called low wing-loading. This helps to keep the raptors aloft.

Vultures fly almost exclusively this way, rarely beating their wings except to takeoff and land. Soaring flight requires all the adaptations necessary for flight in general, with some special variations.

The architectural design of all birds has been guided by anatomical and physiological adjustments that allow flight. Several of these adjustments address weight reduction and power promotion. Flying birds have greatly reduced their weight by developing a light but strong and elastic skeleton composed of thin, hollow bones. To increase the strength of this fragile frame, several bones that normally are separate in other animals have been fused at critical points, and some longer bones and skull bones are reinforced by an internal construction that resembles the struts of an airplane wing. Feathers, required for both aerodynamics and insulation, are light yet remarkably strong—

*Some researchers believe feathers may have evolved first as an insulator and later were adapted for flight.*
*Photograph by Stephen Trimble*

The soaring scavengers and eagles are the largest of all the raptors, and the soaring buteos rank among the largest of hawks. This is no accident. Soaring birds must be sufficiently massive to maintain momentum and stability in erratic air currents. They also must be able to maneuver adroitly, responding quickly and sensitively when the currents change. Fingerlike, slotted primary feather splayed at the ends of their wings help them to fly slowly, with maximum lift, so they can spiral tightly in pillars of rising warm air. A full forty percent of the condor's wing is slotted, contributing to its status as the champion of soaring raptors. All these adaptations make for a slow and steady flier, one not suited for high-speed or extended chases. Soaring raptors usually hunt ground-dwelling mammals or fish, relying on surprise to catch their prey. These birds rarely get a second chance if they miss the first time.

In contrast, falcons and the accipiter hawks are adapted for high-speed, maneuvering flight. These raptors commonly hunt other birds on the wing, relying on blinding speed to catch and kill their prey. The accipters—the sharp-shinned hawk, Cooper's hawk, and the northern goshawk—all have relatively short, rounded wings that they beat rapidly in flight. These short wings, combined with long tails, allow them to maneuver quickly, dodging after birds through the branches and trees of their favored forest habitats. Not surprisingly, the forest-dwelling owls tend to have relatively short wings for maneuverability as well.

Falcons have developed long, narrow, pointed wings to produce lift with little drag, and their body weight tends to be high in relation to wing area. They maneuver adroitly and fly with great speed, but it is their streaking dive that sets them apart. The peregrine falcon, the champion of high-speed divers, is probably the fastest bird alive. Some biologists estimate that peregrines approach 180 miles per hour in near vertical dives. Although peregrines have never been clocked scientifically at anywhere near that rate, anecdotal evidence for high speed abounds. For instance, the Grand Canyon peregrine that we watched stoop on a swallow from 3,200 feet reached river level in a matter of seconds, its body reduced to a blur and a ripping sound as it sliced downward through the air. We counted as it fell ... one-thousand-one ... one-thousand-two ... one-thousand-three ... and estimated

*Peregrine falcons fly rapidly and dive after prey birds at speeds approaching 180 miles per hour. Photograph by F.K. Schleicher for VIREO*

*Soaring birds can maintain momentum and stability in erratic air currents. Photograph by Denver A. Bryan*

*Great horned owls strike silently. Photograph by G. van Frankenhuyzen for Cornell Laboratory of Ornithology*

*Short-eared owls usually hunt at night, but they can be active any time of the day. Photograph by W. Perry Conway*

a speed in excess of 200 miles per hour. This figure is hardly accurate, but the bird was moving fast enough to leave experienced peregrine biologists dumbstruck.

## NOCTURNAL ADAPTATIONS

Owls own the night. In fact, of all predators, owls are among the most perfectly adapted to hunt during the dark hours. Guided by acute hearing and eyes evolved to see in the dimmest light, nocturnal owls fly soundlessly to the kill. Of course, not all owls hunt exclusively at night; some species, like the great horned owl, are crepuscular, hunting most actively at dawn and dusk. A few other species, like the burrowing and pygmy-owls, are active during the full light of day. But owls are usually nocturnal, and their anatomy and appearance reflect this.

The plumage of most owls runs to softly mottled browns and grays, sometimes mixed with black or white. Owls have little need for the bright colors that so many diurnal birds develop for visual signaling. Instead, their subdued, variegated plumage blends invisibly into night shadows. Soft colors conceal owls visually; soft feathers conceal them aurally. Like all nocturnal hunters, owls must move silently to surprise keen-hearing prey during the still hours of night. And owls do fly quietly, much more quietly than any other bird. The sound of their wings is so faint and so low in frequency that it cannot be heard by most animals, nor can it be detected by sensitive recording equipment.

Scientists attribute this ghostly flight to three characteristics. First, the owl's primary feathers on the ends of its wings differ in structure from those of other birds. The feather's leading edge is serrated, presenting a soft, saw-toothed surface. This, combined with a fringed trailing edge, appears to reduce the usual vortex noise of air slipping over a wing. Sound is further muffled by a downy upper surface on the owl's feathers. Low wing-loading also contributes to the owl's silent flight. Its relatively large wings in relation to its body weight provide considerable buoyancy, allowing the bird to fly with minimum flapping motion—hence less noise. As one might expect, the most nocturnal owls are the quietest flyers, while the more diurnal species, like the burrowing and pygmy-owls, are the noisiest.

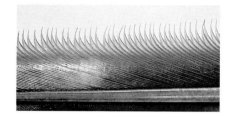

*Above: The small saw-whet owl is well adapted to hunt at night. Note his large eyes and pronounced circular facial disk. Photograph by Joe Sharber Right: The saw-toothed leading edge of owl feathers probably muffle sound. Photograph by Lang Elliott for Cornell Laboratory of Ornithology.*

## THE OWL'S VISION

The nocturnal owl's large, forward-facing eyes are another adaptation for night hunting. No other bird, and possibly no other animal, can see as well in very dim light. One experimenter estimates that the barn-owl's visual threshold (the minimum light needed to discern objects) is 35 times lower than the lowest threshold reported for humans. The visual threshold for other owls may be as much as 100 times lower than man's. The explanation for this acute sensitivity lies in the physiology of the owl's eye.

First, as in all raptors, the eye tends to be extraordinarily large for the size of the animal. A large eye size offers several advantages for nocturnal vision. The larger the cornea and pupillary area at the front of the eye, the more light it will gather. The larger the retina at the back of the eye, the more visual cells it will contain. In the owl, an unusually high ratio of these cells are rods—the cells sensitive to low light intensities. This means that the night-hunting owls have sacrificed the visual acuity provided by cones (high resolution and color perception) for the sensitivity in very dim light provided by rods. These adaptations are important, but the greatest advantage of the owl eye for light sensitivity appears to be its long, tubular shape. This shape allows for a long focal length to produce a large image on the retina, while keeping the overall volume of the eye at a minimum. If the eye were globular in shape, like that of a diurnal raptor, a comparable focal length would require a much larger eye overall—an eye too big for the owl to accommodate. Only owls, in all the animal kingdom, have struck upon this space-saving solution.

## THE OWL'S HEARING

All these adaptations help the owl to see in dim light, but researchers have discovered that at least one owl, the barn-owl, can locate and strike prey in the complete absence of light—in total darkness. Apparently, the owl's skill as a night hunter is due in large part to an exceptional ability to pinpoint and track sound. In repeated tests conducted in light-tight rooms, barn-owls were able to locate faint sounds within one to two degrees on both the horizontal and vertical planes. To eliminate the possibility that the owls were tracking the heat or odor of their prey, researchers strung a rumpled wad of paper behind a mouse, then released the rodent to scurry across a foam rubber floor. In every case, the owl struck the rustling paper rather than the warm and odoriferous, but silent, mouse.

This extraordinary ability to hear very faint sound and to locate it precisely in a spatial grid is made possible by a series of unusual adaptations. Perhaps the most interesting and unusual is the asymmetry of ear openings found in many owls. The right and left ear openings often differ in shape, size, and location on the bird's head. For example, the barn-owl's right ear opening is lower and tilted upward. The left ear opening is higher and tilted downward. This asymmetry allows sound to arrive at the ears at slightly different times and intensities.

To understand how this helps the owl to locate prey, imagine a mouse running through the underbrush beneath a perched bird. If the mouse moves down relative to the owl, or closer to it, its sound becomes louder in the left ear relative to the right. If the mouse moves up, or away from the owl, its sound becomes louder in the right ear. All the owl has to do is adjust its head so that the sound level is equal in both ears to find the correct elevation in the vertical plane. To pinpoint the sound source in the horizontal plane, or azimuth, the owl precisely measures the difference in time it takes a sound to reach its right ear and its left ear. A barn-owl can detect a time lag between its ears as fleeting as 10 millionth of a second.

We know that owls require both ears, or binaural sensitivity, to locate their prey accurately. In experiments where researchers blocked the right ear of a barn-owl, the bird consistently missed its target, striking short and to the left. When they blocked the left ear, the owl struck far and to the right. To process the complex binaural information being received, an owl devotes a large portion of its brain to the hearing function, with more nerves concentrated in the auditory region than in any other bird studied. Much to their astonishment, neurological researchers have discovered that an owl actually develops an auditory map in its brain. The bird can replicate its external environment upon an internal network of neurons (nerve cells). A sound received from the front of the owl excites neurons in the front of the network, sounds from the sides excite neurons in the lateral parts of the network, and so on. No other animal is known to produce such maps.

Although these adaptations for precise sound localization are impressive, they are only part of the story. Owls, particularly the most nocturnal species, also have developed the ability to hear the faintest sounds and the widest range of frequencies known among birds. The most apparent adaptation for these skills is the classic owl face. All owls to some degree possess a roughly circular or heart-shaped facial disk composed of stiff, bristly feathers covered by a layer of more delicate feathers. The disk acts like a satellite dish, collecting, amplifying, and directing sound waves toward large ear openings. Strongly nocturnal owls, like the barn-owl and the saw-whet owl, have pronounced facial disks. The least nocturnal have minimal disks.

In the barn-owl, the ear openings are located in long troughs that further concentrate and direct sound. And to catch the smallest rustle or squeak from behind or below the owl's perch, a movable ear flap borders the opening to function like a hand cupped behind the human ear. Captured sounds are then amplified and carried to the inner ear by unusually large eardrums and middle ear bones.

To make maximum use of both its sensitive eyesight and its keen hearing to locate prey, an owl can swivel its head an astonishing 270 degrees. To track something moving behind it, the owl will first twist its head as far one way as possible, then spin it all the way in the other direction to regain its target. The movement can be so swift that humans cannot see it. This led to the long-held myth that owls can swivel their heads a full 360 degrees and more. Of course, were this true, birds would be twisting their heads right off their bodies—a practice Nature would frown upon.

*The golden eagle hunts the open range and sparse woodlands of the plateau. Photograph by Dick Canby*

*Cliffs like these in Coal Mine Canyon provide nesting sites for prairie and peregrine falcons. Photograph by Tom Danielsen*

*Above: The barn-owl, a nocturnal rodent hunter, prefers to nest in old buildings. Photograph by John Hendrickson*
*Left: Prairie falcons forage in open sagebrush or grassland terrain and nest on cliff ledges.*
*Photograph by W. Perry Conway*

# CHANGING HABITATS AND ENDANGERED SPECIES

Environments are never static. They change because of human interference; they change despite human interference. Raptors, since they prey on a wide range of animals up and down the food chain, are among the first animals to register such alterations. Sometimes, they respond with burgeoning population growth; sometimes, with decline—even extinction. We can see evidence of this responsiveness among every raptor group on the Colorado Plateau. Bald eagles and peregrine falcons, once decimated to near extinction throughout their range, today are showing remarkable signs of recovery. But now, two old-growth forest dwelling raptors, the northern goshawk and the spotted owl, appear to be suffering because timber and grazing management practices are despoiling their habitats. Ironically, their loss may turn out to be the red-tailed hawk's and the great horned owl's gain. Each of these situations offers a complex and instructive tale. We will get to those in a moment; but first, let us look to the past, to the Pleistocene, when two giant birds skimmed the skies over Grand Canyon.

Fifteen thousand years ago, give or take a few years, a bird of prey none of us will ever see soared among the buttes and cliffs of Grand Canyon, scanning the landscape for its next meal. This long-extinct, predaceous carnivore boasted a 12-foot wingspan and probably stalked small animals, swallowing them whole. He was *Teratornis merriami*—literally, "monster" or "wonder" bird. We know teratorns once lived in the Grand Canyon because their bones have been found in Stanton's Cave, a limestone cavern near river level, 32 miles downstream from Lees Ferry. Many more, and much larger, teratorn remains have been recovered in California, Nevada, and even in South America, where species of the family achieved wing spans of 26 feet, weighed in at 175 pounds, and stood over 6 feet tall!

The teratorn was not the only winged titan in Grand Canyon during the Pleistocene. Fossil bones of at least two species of condor, one now extinct, the other nearly so, have been discovered in eight different canyon caves. All remains date from 9,500 to 22,000 years ago, the waning days of the Ice Age. Apparently

condors were once common on the Colorado Plateau, just as they were throughout what is now the southern United States. But as of this writing, only two California condors, both young birds bred in captivity, fly free. What happened to the teratorns and the condors? Why did the big birds all but disappeared some 10,000 years ago.

The answer lies in our ever-changing environment. Teratorns probably succumbed to climatic change, a warming and drying trend that took place at the end of the Ice Age throughout the bird's range. Increasing aridity almost certainly decimated the teratorn's food supply. Reduction of the food supply undoubtedly affected condors as well, but the circumstances may have been a bit different. Researchers hypothesize that during the Pleistocene large populations of scavengers feasted on the carcasses of megafauna—giant mammals like the ground sloths, camels, woolly mammoths, and mastodons that dominated the period. These big animals died out at the end of the Ice Age, possibly because of climatic change but more probably from overkill by growing numbers of human big-game hunters. Whatever the cause, with the demise of the large mammals went many of the large avian scavengers as well. The California condor survived but was reduced to a relatively small population in the extreme western United States, where the birds fed on dead marine animals, deer, elk, and, eventually, cattle. The few condors spotted near the western edge of the Colorado Plateau in the nineteenth century belonged to this group.

We have every reason to believe that the remnant California condor population was stable, even thriving, until American settlers swarmed into the Pacific West during the 1800s. Then, numbers declined rapidly. By 1890, one ornithologist was already predicting extinction. The principal cause was shooting—senseless, malicious shooting. These birds did not threaten stock; they were not eaten; they just presented large, slow-moving targets.

Lead poisoning from swallowing bullet fragments along with carrion took its toll as well. So did power line electrocutions, DDT, and strychnine from poisoned bait. The condor population plummeted until

*Rancher Bill Osborne holds an injured red-tailed hawk that he and his wife helped to rehabilitate. The bird had been shot but recovered sufficiently to be released. Although protected by law, raptors still suffer from human predation. Photograph by Jonathan A. Meyers*

by 1985 only six birds remained in the wild. The following year, the number was down to three. With the species teetering near extinction, the U.S. Fish and Wildlife Service and the California Fish and Game Commission decided to trap the last free California condors, add them to the couple of dozen birds already in zoos, and start a captive breeding program.

So far, it appears that their decision was the right one. As of January 1992, fifty-two birds have been bred, and two of these have already been reintroduced into the wild. Wildlife biologists hope that by educating the public about the need to protect condors, by providing untainted meat, and by encouraging the use of lead-free bullets for hunting, they can assist the newly released condors and their successors in their efforts to survive and breed in a natural habitat.

This habitat includes the Grand Canyon. If the California condor breeding program continues to be successful, some young birds may be released in or near Grand Canyon, where they will find abundant nesting sites, water, and large tracts of land free of hunters, power lines, and other hazards. Food will have to be supplied by wildlife managers on a regular basis, perhaps in perpetuity. But that may be the case wherever the condor is reintroduced. The once boundless, natural world of the free condor is gone forever. If this species is to survive, it will only be with our assistance. The future is uncertain, but if we choose to help, perhaps the California condor once again will fly over the Colorado Plateau.

*Bald eagles were nearly wiped out by human persecution and the use of DDT. Photograph by John Hendrickson*

## THE BALD EAGLE, THE PEREGRINE FALCON, AND DDT

Famous naturalist John James Audubon was lamenting the rapid decline of the bald eagle as early as the 1840s. He suspected the cause was related to human predation on bison and other favored game species that carrion-feeding eagles sometimes depended upon during winter. Peregrine falcon populations in the nineteenth century were probably dwindling as well, though no one seems to have remarked on it at the time. The peregrines had to have been hard hit by the decimation and eventual extinction of the passenger pigeon—a species that once numbered in the billions and almost certainly formed the falcon's principal food base in eastern North America. Significant raptor mortality resulted both indirectly and directly from the indiscriminate killing by heavily armed settlers of anything that flew, walked, or ran. Especially hated were "chicken hawks," a sobriquet for almost any bird of prey. The war against eagles in particular really took off in the latter nineteenth and early twentieth centuries when livestock spread over the grasslands of the American West.

So intense has been misguided human paranoia of winged predators that by the early 1950s approximately 128,000 pairs of bald eagle legs had been turned in for bounties in Alaska, and from the mid-1950s to the early 1960s, more than 20,000 bald and golden eagles were shot from airplanes over sheep ranches in Texas. Golden eagles are certainly capable of killing young sheep, but the poor, misunderstood bald eagle eats mostly fish and carrion, and all that killing and destruction accomplished nothing except to satisfy some level of human rage against fellow predators.

Raptor death statistics of forty and fifty years ago from other states and countries caused by deliberate shootings, poisoning, trapping, and nest destruction are equally appalling. However, the menace that almost succeeded in driving the eagles and peregrines to extinction was not human predation at all, but the introduction of chlorinated hydrocarbon pesticides during the mid-1940s.

Dichloro-diphenyl-trichloro-ethane, more commonly known as DDT, remains one of the most pow-

*Peregrine falcons were so decimated by DDT that by the mid-1960s they had disappeared from most of the United States. Photograph by W. Perry Conway*

*DDT caused eggshell thinning to the point that incubating adult peregrines frequently crushed their eggs. Photograph by W. Perry Conway*

erful and successful insecticides used against disease-spreading house flies and mosquitos and against generic agricultural pests. The chemical, because of its persistence and tendency to "bioaccumulate," was banned in the United States and most of Europe by the mid-1970s. Many industrial nations, however, including the United States, continue to manufacture the chemical for export into third world countries, where, notwithstanding its lethality in the environment, it is praised as a "miracle" insecticide. In some areas of the world, the use of DDT has virtually eliminated the scourge of malaria and has helped to reduce human starvation through increased crop production.

But DDT leaves a deadly legacy. Within a decade of its first use in the western world, this insecticide and its widespread breakdown product (DDE) had virtually wiped out North American and European populations of peregrine falcons and had significantly reduced the numbers of North American bald eagles. The peregrine falcon was the hardest hit. By the mid-1960s, peregrines had vanished east of the Great Plains and south of Canada. They had largely disappeared from the northern Rocky Mountains and coastal areas of the western seaboard as well. Although our documentation is not as thorough, declines also were evident in the Southwest.

Once ornithologists noticed that the eagles and peregrines were in serious decline, it only took a few years for some of the more astute biologists to find the cause and effect relationship between the introduction of the chlorinated hydrocarbon pesticides and the loss of birds. The insidious nature of DDT/DDE is such that the chemicals increasingly concentrate as they pass up the food chain from prey to predator. The highest level predators, like birds of prey, accumulate in their bodies pesticide residues from every prey item consumed along the chain. Studies on avian tissues and eggshells have shown that within one year of the introduction of DDT in 1946, accumulation of its breakdown product, DDE, in peregrine falcons was sufficiently high to interfere with reproductive success. A landmark study by retired banker Charles Broley on Florida bald eagles documented a perilous decline in young birds—also within a single year after DDT was first used there for mosquito control.

The actual physiological influence of DDT/DDE poisoning in the birds of prey was not understood immediately, and the initial expressions of concern led to astounding claims by economic entomologists and other agricultural interests on the safety and world-wide economic importance of DDT. Some pesticide salesmen even went so far as to publicly consume the allegedly benign white power by the spoonful with no immediate and apparent consequences. What we know today, however, clearly contradicts the posture of the chemical industry in the decades preceding a ban on DDT use. Humans can apparently handle the break-down products of DDT with little outward damage, though the jury is still out on long-term impacts. In birds, however, DDE concentration results in reduced sexual drive, including weak courtship behavior, late-ness in getting nests started, weak pair bonds, and generally decreased abilities as functioning parents. The greatest problem, though, is that DDE causes eggshell thinning by inhibiting enzymes that allow calcium to be delivered to the oviduct where shell membranes are produced. Without the normal amounts of calcium in the eggs, shells are weak and easily crushed by the incubating adults. Once the egg is crushed in the nest, the adults eat the egg contents and reproduction fails.

During the height of the era of declining peregrine populations, biologists determined that eggshell thick-ness and weight was about 25 percent reduced from eggs laid prior to the introduction of DDT. Today in Grand Canyon National Park, though the peregrine falcons apparently are healthy and reproducing abun-dantly, eggshell thickness is still reduced from pre-1946 norms. Eggs from two eyries, measured in 1988, more than fifteen years after DDT was banned in this country, showed a reduction in normal shell thickness of about 12 percent. This may be an alarming indica-tion of the chemical's persistence in the environment. But, if so, a 12-percent reduction in shell thickness apparently is not sufficient to prevent successful breed-ing. The eggshell fragments could also have been old ones, predating the 1988 hatch. Peregrines will use the same eyries year after year.

It took a decade from discovery of the linkage to ban-ning of the chemical. The story of this environmental sleuthing represents one of the more successful attempts at applying scientific methodology to solving disas-trous ecological problems. Today, ever-growing popula-tions of bald eagles and peregrine falcons are reclaiming areas from which they once disappeared.

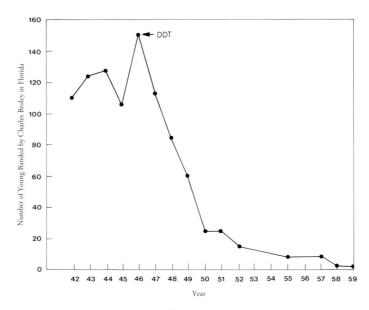

*The number of nesting Florida bald eagles banded by Charles Broley began to decline dramatically after the introduction of the pesticide DDT in 1946. The decline reflects a decrease in the productivity of eagles, not in Broley's effort. From:* The Bald Eagle: Haunts and Habitats of a Wilderness Monarch, *John M. Gerrard and Gary R. Bartolotti. Smithsonian Institution Press, 1988. Courtesy of Smithsonian Institution Press*

*Since the banning of DDT, falcon chicks like these little prairie falcons can once again be found in their cliff eyries. Photograph by Rich Kirchner*

Recent studies of peregrine populations in Grand Canyon by Dr. Bryan T. Brown have documented an astounding fluorescence of the species in the Southwest. A 1985 peregrine falcon recovery plan drafted by the United States Fish and Wildlife Service estimated that recovery of the Rocky Mountain and southwestern populations would be considered complete when more than 180 pairs were found west of the Mississippi River. By 1989, over 100 pairs had been found in the Colorado River drainage alone, with 71 of these nesting in Grand Canyon National Park. No detailed studies on peregrines in Grand Canyon were conducted prior to the introduction of DDT, but years of bird observations in the park since the early 1900s indicated only rare occurrences of the falcon. Unless early ornithologists simply missed the birds, which is unlikely, peregrines were never common there. Today, however, the density of peregrines in the Grand Canyon represents the largest population of this species on a single land-management unit in the contiguous United States. The removal of DDT from the environment clearly has had a profound affect on the restoration of peregrine populations in general, but to explain why these falcons should be so successful in the Grand Canyon now, when apparently they were not historically, suggests that other factors may be at work.

*Peregrines falcon. Photograph by W. Perry Conway*

*In Grand Canyon National Park, changes in the Colorado River caused by Glen Canyon Dam upstream may inadvertently have helped the peregrine falcon and the bald eagle. Photograph by Jonathan A. Meyers*

31

## BALD EAGLES, PEREGRINE FALCONS, AND GLEN CANYON DAM

While raptor biologists in the early 1960s were struggling with cause and effect relationships between DDT and population declines, something quite different and seemingly unrelated was occurring on the Colorado Plateau—something that would profoundly influence the Grand Canyon's bald eagle and peregrine falcon populations. In 1963, the floodgates of Glen Canyon Dam closed, creating Lake Powell and forever changing the Colorado River below the dam.

Major dams, especially a 710-foot-high structure like Glen Canyon Dam, are always accompanied by a certain amount of environmental destruction. Usually, this can be measured by the amount of free-flowing river and associated riparian habitats that are drowned as the impoundment fills and what was once a river becomes a lake. It took almost twenty years for the reservoir behind Glen Canyon Dam to fill. Once that process was complete, a 186-mile-long lake with over 1,960 miles of shoreline was created. The loss of the riverine ecosystems beneath Lake Powell was loudly lamented by some, while others, with equal passion, celebrated the economic benefits of the engineering feat. Neither the promoters nor the detractors of the dam considered or anticipated alterations in Colorado River habitats downstream of the dam that would occur once the floodgates were closed. It appears now, however, that along with some very serious detrimental impacts to the downstream riverine ecosystem, the dam has provided, at least temporarily, new opportunities for peregrine falcons and bald eagles.

The basis for these new opportunities can be traced directly to a change in the river's primary productivity (its capacity to produce nutrients that support life). Shortly after the dam became operational, the once muddy river ran clear, completely free of sediment. Within a year, the "new" river was not only crystal clear but icy cold as well because the water released through the dam was drawn from penstocks far below Lake Powell's surface, where warming rays of sunlight never penetrated. With the muddy water gone, primary productivity of the river increased at least tenfold. Rays of sunlight, once reflected off a muddy river surface, penetrated deeply to the river bottom where algal growth flourished and provided a foundation for a new, different, and highly productive aquatic food web. Within the clear and cold water habitats of the new river, introduced rainbow trout rapidly came to dominate the fishery, an event that set the stage for an invasion of bald eagles.

*Rainbow trout spawning in Nankoweap Creek attract migrating bald eagles. Photograph by Tom Brownold*

*Glen Canyon Dam, fifteen miles upstream of the Grand Canyon. Photograph by Stewart Aitchison*

*Left: Nankoweap Creek joins the Colorado River
52 miles below the head of the Grand Canyon.
Photograph by Christa J. Sadler
Below: The Colorado River in the Grand
Canyon downstream of Nankoweap Creek.
Photograph by Heather Green*

Intensive bird surveys along the river corridor in Grand Canyon performed by Museum of Northern Arizona biologists throughout the 1970s and early 1980s provide a base from which to interpret changes in the distribution and density patterns of several species, including the bald eagle. Records kept almost every year from 1971 to 1983 do not indicate that bald eagles used the river corridor at that time. Occasionally, one or two migrants would be seen flying over the canyon or on the rims, but eagles were never seen along the river. Suddenly, during the winter of 1985-86, four eagles appeared at Nankoweap Creek, a small tributary stream 52 miles below Lees Ferry. Thereafter, ever-increasing numbers of bald eagles showed up at Nankoweap every winter until 1992. Concentrations of eagles peaked in 1990 and 1991 when as many as 26 individuals were clustered within a few miles of Nankoweap Creek.

We are not sure how soon after the dam had changed the river that rainbow trout began to spawn in Nankoweap Creek and a few other Grand Canyon tributaries. It is clear, however, that by the late 1970s the spawning runs were spectacular to witness. A typical run in late December would be characterized by 400-500 large adult (2 to 5 lbs.) trout struggling upstream in the shallow water of the creek. Sometimes, there were so many fish in the creek that it looked as though one could walk across the stream on their bright green backs. While hundreds of these fish filled the stream, hundreds more swarmed in the river at the tributary mouth, waiting their chance to enter the crowded stream and spawn.

Ravens found this winter food source first, but once eagles had made the discovery, migrants on their way north to breed stopped at the new lunch counter. They intimidated the ravens and stayed to enjoy the abundant fresh fish provided by Glen Canyon Dam. Raptor biologist Rich Glinski of the Arizona Game and Fish Department, who witnessed the ever-increasing concentration of eagles, predicted that if the trout spawning patterns were to remain constant, bald eagles would eventually set up housekeeping and breed in Grand Canyon. Glinski now believes that these optimistic predictions may have been premature. In the past few years, rainbow trout spawning has grown numerically smaller and seasonally later. In 1992, only 100 or so trout ran up Nankoweap

Creek, and they did not even begin the spawn until early March. It is no accident, then, that during the winter of 1992 fewer eagles were found at Nankoweap than in any year since 1985. It appears that rainbow trout are now in serious decline in the Grand Canyon. Their declining numbers are the subject of an intensive study by Arizona's Game and Fish Department and the Glen Canyon Environmental studies group led by David Wegner.

What does the future hold for bald eagles in Grand Canyon? Only time and additional study will tell.

Increased aquatic productivity in the Colorado River has provided new food resources for the peregrine. So have dam-related changes in terrestrial habitats along the river's edge. Before Glen Canyon Dam, annual beach-scouring floods prevented the establishment of riparian or streamside vegetation on all but the highest river terraces. Once the dam was in place, scouring floods were mostly controlled. Instead of raging torrents that once ravaged the lower terraces at an average rate of 100,000 cubic feet per second (cfs) every spring, post-dam water releases rarely exceeded the powerplant capacity of 31,500 cfs. Within days of floodgate closure, woody riparian vegetation—tamarisk, willow, arrowweed, and seep-willow—began to colonize once barren beaches. New riparian vegetation provided homes for nesting birds, amphibians and reptiles, and small mammals. It also provided habitat for the billions of black flies and other aquatic insects emerging from the river. And, most important to our peregrine falcon story, the combination of insects and vegetation provided new and rich feeding areas for insectivorous white-throated swifts, violet-green swallows, and several species of bats—critical food resources for peregrine falcons in Grand Canyon.

Peregrine falcon densities along the river corridor during the 1970s and early 1980s were relatively low. A typical survey of the 225 miles from Lees Ferry to Diamond Creek would find four to six individual birds. Interestingly, densities of a close cousin to the peregrine, the American kestrel, were very high—with individuals or pairs occurring almost every river mile. Today, we find a pair of peregrines every three to five miles of river, but the kestrels have virtually disappeared. What happened?

We believe now that the kestrel became easy prey for growing numbers of its faster, bigger, and more

*Adult and juvenile bald eagles join a raven near the confluence of Nankoweap Creek and the mouth of the Colorado River. Photograph by Tom Brownold*

aggressive cousin. Kestrels typically hang low in the canyon compared to the peregrine, frequently crossing the river in pursuit of insects and lizards. With the river below them and ever-increasing numbers of peregrines commanding the skies above, the kestrels must have become "sitting ducks" for their hungry relatives. This conclusion is supported by hard evidence. Remnants of kestrels have been found in a Grand Canyon eyrie.

Today, as we watch the foraging activities of peregrines in the river corridor, we often see a peregrine or two diving into a flock of swifts and swallows, capturing and eating three and four of the smaller birds on the wing before wandering away. Dr. Tom Cade, the preeminent peregrine biologist, recently accompanied us on a canyon falcon survey and observed a peregrine feeding in a flock of bats. The bird ate numerous bats within a twenty-minute period. Have the swifts, swallows, and bats increased in density as the river primary productivity increased? Has this led to a remarkable concentration of a falcon once thought to be near extinction? All the evidence leads us to believe such is the case, but the story of the changing environment of Grand Canyon below Glen Canyon Dam is far from complete. The one thing we can probably count on is continuing change.

*Peregrine falcon covering (mantling) prey. Photograph by W. Perry Conway*

## NORTHERN GOSHAWKS, MEXICAN SPOTTED OWLS, AND OLD GROWTH FORESTS

Northern goshawks and Mexican spotted owls on the Colorado Plateau share two characteristics: they reach their highest densities in old-growth forests, and they seem to be rapidly decreasing in numbers. Reasons for declining populations in these two species are indisputably linked to logging activities and the attendant removal or modification of habitat. Suitable habitat for goshawks and spotted owls on the plateau is almost exclusively restricted to U.S. Forest Service land, with a much smaller amount found on National Park Service administrative units. A very small amount of owl habitat is also found on Bureau of Land Management land. The fate of these deep-forest raptors on the Colorado Plateau is directly influenced by current and future management practices in federally administered forests.

One would think that with all the modern-day advances in ecological understanding and sophisticated timber and range harvesting strategies, a balanced consumption of natural resources could also provide a level of protection for all forest animals. This is not the case. Forests are being consumed by

*Ponderosa forest. Photograph by Dick Canby*

*Goshawks rank among the most effective avian predators of the deep forests. Photograph by Rick Kline for Cornell Laboratory of Ornithology*

*Logging of deep-forest habitats threaten both the goshawk and the spotted owl. Photograph by Stewart Aitchison*

timber harvest, and to a lesser extent by management for livestock grazing, at a rate in excess of the ecosystem's natural ability to restore itself. In the last decade, from thirty to forty percent of habitat known to be suitable for goshawks and spotted owls has been rendered unsuitable. Combine that statistic with the fact that in the next five decades demand for forest products will increase by an estimated thirty percent. Unless something is done, the future does not look bright for goshawks and spotted owls on the Colorado Plateau.

That something may be getting done, however. National forest management practices have been challenged in the Southwest in recent years, resulting in efforts to reduce natural resource harvests and save more of the forests for the animals. To gather much needed information, the Forest Service now employs teams of biologists to survey all national forests in the Southwest systematically for Mexican spotted owls, determining both their density and nesting locations. One positive outgrowth of recent attention to both the goshawk and the spotted owl has been to identify clearly in the scientific and popular literature the relationships between timber harvests and declining raptor numbers. While these developments show movement in the right direction, separate petitions recently submitted to the U.S. Fish and Wildlife Service to provide threatened or endangered species status to the northern goshawk and the Mexican spotted owl have had mixed results.

*Spotted owls are important indicators of the health of old-growth forests. Photograph by John Hendrickson*

## NORTHERN GOSHAWK

Northern goshawks are known to be "indicator species" of overall forest ecology, and when they begin to disappear, there is a strong possibility that the entire forest ecosystem is in decline. All of the forest-dwelling hawks of the genus Accipiter, including the goshawk and the Cooper's and sharp-shinned hawks, are known to undergo fluctuations in population size, density, and nesting success. Natural factors, usually related to prey availability, often cause these fluctuations. For the goshawk on the Kaibab Plateau of northern Arizona, dramatic changes in Kaibab squirrel numbers, which sometimes relate to climatic patterns and to pine crop success, can result in substan-

tial differences in how many raptors are fledged and ultimately survive.

Many investigators now believe that the past several years of declining goshawk numbers, and to a lesser extent similar patterns in Cooper's and sharp-shinned hawks, are not a function of natural factors but of human-caused habitat modifications. Timber management practices are removing the old-growth, densely canopied woodlands especially favored by the goshawk. Old-growth stands are harvested selectively, leaving the forest with relatively sterile, even-age stands of smaller, younger trees. After an old forest is cut, it sometimes becomes more suitable for red-tailed hawks

*Old-growth forest habitats are endangered. Photograph by Dale Schicketanz*

*Great horned owl. Photograph by A. Carey for VIREO*

*Jackrabbit, an important prey species on the plateau. Photograph by Robert Campbell*

and great horned owls than for the old forest raptors that once claimed it as home. Indeed, as the forest conversion proceeds, red-tailed hawk and great horned owl populations have been increasing in density by as much as two percent per year for the past twenty years in Arizona and New Mexico. To compound the insult, both of these species are formidable predators on young goshawks and spotted owls.

The vulnerability of the goshawk outside of its preferred dense forest habitat is tragically epitomized by the recent demise of Flagstaff falconer Joe Sharber's trained bird. Sharber and his adult gos were hunting jackrabbits in open piñon-juniper woodland, and the bird, hot after its quarry, charged full speed into a juniper thicket. As the bird came out the other side, it was met, not by a jackrabbit but by a pair of golden eagles. The eagles were tracking the same jackrabbit but were soaring high above the action on which both falconer and goshawk were intent. Having the advantage, the eagles took their best shot, pounced, and quickly killed both rabbit and bird. Sharber was left with some bloody goshawk tail feathers, a patch of rabbit fur, and partial remains of the leather jesses that had once tethered his hawk. Out of its normal habitat of dense canopied forests, the goshawk was exposed to predation, something that must take place only rarely under natural conditions.

Although the U.S. Fish and Wildlife Service does not argue with the fact that declining numbers of goshawks on the Colorado Plateau present a serious problem for the survival of the species in this area, they recently declined to list the goshawk as "threatened" or "endangered" in response to a petition recently submitted by a coalition of environmental groups. Their justification rested on a technicality. They maintained that we lack compelling evidence to show that the goshawks in Arizona, New Mexico, Colorado, and Utah together form a distinct and isolated population. They do not contest evidence correlating the sharply declining numbers of goshawks in the conifer forests of the West to timber harvesting, forest conversion to agriculture, and interruption of forest succession by fire suppression. However, one of the conditions of the Endangered Species Act requires that to be a listable entity, a species or populations of a species must be geographically isolated and, hence, genetically distinct.

At present, the northern goshawk's official status is a "Category 2 Candidate Species." This means that we have evidence to indicate vulnerability but lack data to support protection under terms of the Act. Environmental groups are frantically attempting to gather the scientific data needed to demonstrate the distinct nature of goshawk populations in the Colorado Plateau states before the bird completely disappears from the area. Success or failure of this effort is at least several years away.

Left: The northern goshawk has the red eye of the accipiter hawks. Photograph by W. Breene for VIREO
Below: Ponderosa forest. Photograph by W. Perry Conway

Above: Pygmy owl, another raptor of the deep forest. Photograph by John Hendrickson
Left: Mixed conifer forest in the high country north of the Grand Canyon. Photograph by Gene Balzer

## MEXICAN SPOTTED OWL

Researchers who have had the opportunity to work with the spotted owl often speak in superlative terms about the bird's beauty, gentleness, tameness, and ghostly silent flight. Youngsters fresh out of the nest are so calm and unaware of life's perils they can easily be approached and captured by hand. This fact alone goes a long way toward explaining the need for relatively inaccessible and dense old-growth nesting areas. Parental hope that their owlets will survive to adulthood must largely be vested in having a well-hidden, densely foliaged nesting area.

Avian taxonomists have not had the same difficulty establishing that Mexican spotted owls are a distinct population that they have had with the northern goshawk. Mexican spotted owls are clearly recognized as one of three distinct subspecies. The northern spotted owl, found mostly in northern California, Oregon, and Washington, is the subspecies around which bitter controversy is raging between environmentalists and timber industry concerns. The northern spotted owl has been listed as "threatened" for some time, and its long-term survival is tied irrevocably to significant reductions in projected timber harvests throughout the Pacific Northwest. Because of "teeth" in the Endangered Species Act and its ability to stop destruction of a listed species' habitat, many in the timber industry claim that owls have become more important than people. Increasing instances of deliberate destruction of northern spotted owls and their nests are a sad commentary on the present conflict over short-term economic gain and long-term preservation of forest ecosystems.

At about the same time conservation groups were soliciting the Fish and Wildlife Service to list northern goshawks, a similar petition was submitted calling for protection of Mexican spotted owls. The owl petition was met with a far more sympathetic review. The agency has determined that spotted owls in Arizona, New Mexico, Colorado, Utah, parts of Texas, and northern Mexico do form a declining, distinct, and isolated population.

Final decisions on listing the Mexican spotted owl as "threatened" will be made late in 1992. Because the habitat types of the spotted owl and the northern goshawk significantly overlap, the goshawk will automatically receive a measure of protection if the owl is listed.

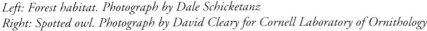

*Left: Forest habitat. Photograph by Dale Schicketanz*
*Right: Spotted owl. Photograph by David Cleary for Cornell Laboratory of Ornithology*

# SOME FINAL THOUGHTS

Through the ages, birds of prey have been either worshiped or reviled by most members of the human race—ironically, itself a predatorial species. Warrior orders for thousands of years have captured and tamed many species of avian predators, training them to hunt, training them to be subservient to human masters. A falconer's dominance over creatures as wild as the wind gives that individual a particular sense of intoxicating power few other accomplishments can provide. Native American legends and ceremonies often echo atavistic sentiments that brother eagle, hawk, and falcon are messengers to and from benevolent gods, while brother owl is often associated with malevolence and death. To fly like the eagle, to be as free as the power of flight allows, has forever been the secret longing of shamans, naturalists, and romantic dreamers. To be fascinated by birds of prey is part of the human condition. But that fascination has not always been benign.

Hatred and fear of birds of prey must have originated with pastoral living, where the loss of a single chicken, lamb, or goat could endanger the welfare of family and farm. In 1881 when those prospectors below the Grand Wash Cliffs caused the senseless death of that condor, they were acting within the mores of the time. People dismissed raptors as vermin, as vicious (even evil) destroyers of "innocent" animal life—and as intolerable competitors of man for domestic

*Open grassland habitat, Government Prairie west of the San Francisco Peaks. Photograph by Stewart Aitchison*

*Sharp-shinned hawk of the genus* Accipiter.
*Photograph by W. Perry Conway*

*Ground-dwelling burrowing owls. Photograph by Rich Kirchner*

stock and wild game. This mythology, based on ignorance and assumed human superiority, has been difficult to overcome. As long as we treated all predators solely as either direct or indirect competitors, we could overlook their beneficial role in ecosystems and ignore their beauty. Instead of seeing the critical role played by avian predators in the natural world, we put bounties on their heads.

Although we now understand the pivotal role that predators, including birds of prey, have in maintaining healthy ecosystems, indiscriminate killing continues, albeit much abated in the last few decades. State and federal laws now mandate the protection of many species and habitats. And a vocal public, long since removed from farm and range, widely believes that a greater public good is served by the protection of predators, even when that protection may result in the loss of a few chickens and sheep. Rather than pay bounty for

a dead eagle, most of us would prefer to provide subsidies to ranchers for predator-related livestock deaths. To anyone losing livestock, however, the situation remains economically threatening, and isolated incidents like the recent poisoning of bald eagles in southern Utah will be with us for a long time.

On the Colorado Plateau, the long-term prospects for birds of prey are generally positive. This is not to say that plateau country is free of threats associated with resource exploitation, energy production, and urbanization. Far from it. All consumptive activities important to sustaining our present industrialized economic system are here and expanding; however, a more balanced and rational approach to development and protection of natural resources is evident in a growing number of Colorado Plateau constituents.

Unparalleled scenic beauty has focused worldwide attention on our area. This visibility alone provides a measure of protection. In addition, eighty-five percent of the land on the Colorado Plateau is either federally administered public land, Indian reservation, or state property. Over two dozen national parks, national monuments, and national recreation areas; fifteen national forests; and ten Bureau of Land Management units leave very little private land onto which the human population can expand without public acquiescence. And even though there are significant differences in land management policies among tribal, park, forest, and range jurisdictions, these areas are virtually guaranteed to remain as vast open spaces, with at least the potential for natural ecosystems to flourish and reach equilibrium. World pressures and common sense demand the protection of this resource. The magnificent raptors of the Colorado Plateau should be the long-term beneficiaries.

43

# RAPTORS OF THE COLORADO PLATEAU: AN ANNOTATED LIST

Most of the birds listed here are raptors commonly seen on the Colorado Plateau. Many of them are permanent residents; some migrate into the region only to breed. Two species, the bald eagle and the rough-legged hawk, only winter in the area. The secondmost rare and elusive bird on the list, the merlin, passes through on its way to the north to breed or to the south to winter. The rarest bird on the list, and one not presently found on the plateau, is the California condor. It is included because it lived here once and may soon again grace the skies over Grand Canyon.

## SPECIES

ORDER FALCONIFORMES
  Family Cathartidae
    Turkey vulture *Cathartes aura.* Common summer resident in all but the most heavily forested habitats. Seen in greatest abundance during spring and fall migrations.
    California condor *Gymnogyps californianus.* Endangered and almost extinct. Formerly a resident in the Grand Canyon area.

  Family Accipitridae
    Osprey *Pandion haliaetus.* Uncommon summer resident and migrant around lakes and streams where abundant forage fish are available.
    Bald eagle *Haliaeetus leucocephalus.* Rare summer transient and sometimes common winter resident, especially around streams and lakes where abundant forage fish are available.
    Northern harrier (Marsh Hawk) *Circus cyaneus.* Relatively common winter visitor in grassland and marshy habitats and rare summer resident in the same habitats.
    Sharp-shinned hawk *Accipiter striatus.* Uncommon summer resident of wooded areas, usually the boreal forests of spruce, aspen, and mixed conifers.
    Cooper's hawk *Accipiter cooperii.* Uncommon summer resident of all forest, woodland, and riparian habitats. Rare winter visitor as well.
    Northern goshawk *Accipiter gentilis.* Uncommon summer and rare winter resident of conifer forests, probably reaching highest densities in ponderosa pine forests.

Swainson's hawk *Buteo swainsoni.* Uncommon summer resident of open grasslands, agricultural fields, and riparian habitats, but more common throughout during spring and fall migrations.

Red-tailed hawk *Buteo jamaicensis.* Common permanent resident in almost all area habitats.
Ferruginous hawk *Buteo regalis.* Rare summer resident and uncommon winter resident of open grasslands and sparse woodlands.
Rough-legged hawk *Buteo lagopus.* Uncommon winter visitor in open grasslands, sagelands, and other open and arid habitats.
Golden eagle *Aquila chrysaetos.* Uncommon permanent resident in mountain areas; uncommon winter visitors move into valley areas.

  Family Falconidae
    American kestrel (Sparrow hawk) *Falco sparverius.* Abundant resident and migrant from alpine to desert habitats.

Merlin (pigeon-hawk) *Falco columbarius*. Rare winter resident and spring and fall migrant in most area habitats. The species may have previously nested in the area. There is an unconfirmed record for Bryce Canyon during June of 1984.

Peregrine falcon *Falco peregrinus*. Once endangered to the point of near extinction, this species is now one of the most common summer residents of high cliffs and solitary mesas, especially in Grand Canyon.

Prairie falcon *Falco mexicanus*. Uncommon resident of open grasslands; sagelands; and other arid, sparsely vegetated areas where nearby cliff habitats offer nest sites.

ORDER STRIGIFORMES

Family Tytonidae

Barn-owl *Tyto alba*. Fairly common permanent resident. Largely associated with open fields, woodlands and along stream banks, especially where old buildings and abandoned mines are found.

Family Strigidae

Flammulated owl *Otus flammeolus*. Common summer resident of coniferous forests. Sometimes very common during fall migrations in ponderosa pine forests.

Western screech-owl *Otus kennicottii*. Rare permanent resident of piñon-juniper woodlands and riparian areas. Spring and fall transient at higher elevations.

Great horned owl *Bubo virginianus*. Most common permanent resident owl. Found in almost all habitats.

Northern pygmy-owl *Glaucidium gnoma*. Uncommon permanent resident of woodlands and forests.

Burrowing owl *Athene cunicularia*. Uncommon summer resident of open fields and high desert areas where prairie dogs and ground squirrels are found.

Spotted owl *Strix occidentalis*. Uncommon-to-rare permanent resident of old-growth conifer forests and deep canyons.

Long-eared owl *Asio otus*. Uncommon to rare. Young birds seem to migrate, but older birds overwinter on breeding grounds in woodlands, conifer forests, and heavily wooded riparian areas.

Short-eared owl *Asio flammeus*. Rare winter visitor in grasslands, marshes, and fields.

Northern saw-whet owl *Aegolius acadicus*. Usually uncommon summer resident of conifer forests; however, population eruptions sometimes occur, reaching relatively high densities.

*Opposite: Swainson's hawk. Photograph by W. Perry Conway*
*Top left: American kestrel. Photograph by John Hendrickson*
*Above: Barn-owls. Photograph by John Hendrickson*

# AUTHORS' NOTE

Occasionally, species of raptors other than those listed above pass through the Colorado Plateau area. These are very rare or accidental occurrences of species normally found far from the plateau. We include them here only as a matter of interest; the birds are not expected to be seen regularly, and some may never be found in the area again.

Sparse records exist for two neotropical migrant species found frequently south of the plateau. The common black-hawk *Buteogallus anthracinus* has been seen a few times in northern Arizona, and a nest was even spotted at Springdale, Utah, near Zion National Park. The zone-tailed hawk *Buteo albonotatus* also has been sighted on the plateau in Arizona, with the northernmost records from the Grand Canyon area.

The red-shouldered hawk *Buteo lineatus* and broadwinged hawk *Buteo platypterus* are accidental visitors or very rare migrants through the area and far from their mostly eastern United States migration routes and breeding areas. The red-shouldered also is found along the coast in Oregon and California.

The gyrfalcon *Falco rusticolus* and the snowy owl *Nyctea scandiaca* occasionally appear on the Colorado Plateau as they move down the continent from their normal breeding grounds in the tundra regions of North America. The movements of both species are known to be very irregular and irruptive in nature and may be caused by climatic factors and prey-base fluctuations on the breeding grounds.

We appreciate the efforts of the following biologists in reviewing this issue of *Plateau*: Bryan T. Brown, Scott Cutler, Richard L. Glinski, R. Roy Johnson, Kenneth A. Kingsley, and G. Scott Mills.

*Clockwise from upper left: Prairie falcon. Photograph by John Hendrickson; Barn-owl. Photograph by John Hendrickson; Flammulated owl. Photograph by R.K. Bowers for VIREO; Merlin. Photograph by John Hendrickson; High desert scrub habitat, Vermilion Cliffs, Arizona. Photograph by Tom Danielsen; California condor. Photograph by Dave Clendenen*

# SELECTED READINGS

Cade, T.J., J.E. Enderson, C.G. Thelander, and C.M. White, eds.
    1988 *Peregrine Falcon Populations: Their Management and Recovery*. Boise, Idaho, The Peregrine Fund, Inc. 949 pp.

Carothers, S.W. and B.T. Brown
    1991 *The Colorado River through Grand Canyon: Natural History and Human Change*. Tucson, University of Arizona Press. 235 pp.

Gerrard, J.M. and G.R. Bortolotti
    1988 *The Bald Eagle: Haunts and Habitats of a Wilderness Monarch*. Washington, D.C., Smithsonian Institution Press. 178 pp.

Johnsgard, P.A.
    1988 *North American Owls: Biology and Natural History*. Washington, D.C., Smithsonian Institution Press. 295 pp.
    1990 *Hawks, Eagles, and Falcons of North America*. Washington, D.C., Smithsonian Institution Press. 403 pp.

Ryser, F.A.
    1985 *Birds of the Great Basin*. Reno, University of Nevada Press. 604 pp.

Terres, J.K.
    1980 *The Audubon Society Encyclopedia of North American Birds*. New York, Alfred Knopf. 1110 pp.

Welty, J.C.
    1962 *The Life of Birds*. Philadelphia, W.B. Saunders. 546 pp.

## Note to Readers

VIREO is an acronym for
Visual Resources for Ornithology, part
of the Academy of Natural Sciences of Philadelphia.

# ABOUT THE AUTHORS

Steven W. Carothers, who received a Ph.D. in Zoology from the University of Illinois, has focused his career on the problems that arise when human activities intersect natural systems. His professional interest in the wildlife and ecology of the Colorado Plateau originated and flourished during a seventeen-year tenure as a research scientist with the Museum of Northern Arizona. Dr. Carothers currently heads SWCA Environmental Consultants, Inc., based in Flagstaff, Arizona. His long list of publications includes *Grand Canyon Birds: Historical Notes, Natural History, and Ecology* and *The Colorado River Through Grand Canyon: Natural History and Human Change*, both co-authored with Bryan T. Brown. Previous contributions to *Plateau* include "Wildlife of the Colorado Plateau."

Dorothy A. House joined the Museum of Northern Arizona staff as librarian nearly eighteen years ago. Like most librarians, Ms. House is a generalist, her interests spanning a multitude of subjects from human history to natural history. In addition to managing the museum's library and archives, she writes, edits, lectures, curates exhibits, and leads hikes and river trips into the Grand Canyon. Her previous contributions to *Plateau* include "Arizona's Grand Canyon." Ms. House holds an M.A. degree in Librarianship from the University of Denver.

Managing Editor: Diana C. Lubick
Editorial Assistant: D.A. Boyd
Design: Libby Jennings
Printing: Land O'Sun
Color Separations: American Color
Typography: MacTypeNet